the Beauty Mix

SIMPLE, SAFE & SOULFUL
SKINCARE RECIPES TO MAKE
IN THE THERMOMIX

NICKY GORDON

Published by The Beauty Dispensary
510 Longreach Road
Longreach NSW 2540 Australia

www.beautydispensary.net

ISBN 978-09944090-4-1

The Thermomix logo is a registered trademark in Australia, owned by Vorwerk International AG. The Beauty Mix has no association or sponsorship with Thermomix in Australia Pty Ltd, or Vorwerk International AG. None of the recipes which appear in this book have been tested or approved by either of those parties.

The views expressed in this work are those of the author and are not sponsored by any particular company unless clearly stated to be so.

The author hereby expressly disclaims any responsibility for any adverse effects that may result from use of advice and recommendations contained in this book.

CONTENTS

INTRODUCTION

In just the same way that wholesome, home-cooked food is better for our bodies than pre-made or processed food, homemade skincare is much better for our skin than mass-produced, store bought products. Manufactured skincare products often contain filler ingredients to lower the cost of production and increase profit for the manufacturer, but unfortunately these additives don't offer much nourishment to our skin and can sometimes be harmful to our bodies.

Everyone who owns a Thermomix knows how effecient and versatile they are. I have been making my own skincare products for many years now, and it was not until the first time I used the Thermomix to make a batch of face cream that I fully appreciated this wonderful appliance in all its glory. It transformed the whole process into an easy, clutter-free experience with perfectly blended and synergised formulas to rival any of the store bought brands. Using the Thermomix to create my homemade concoctions has truly revolutionised the whole procedure. Never has making skincare products at home been as simple and straightforward as it is now. Creating luscious creams, lotions, scrubs, serums and balms using the Thermomix is fuss free and uncomplicated.

Not all of the recipes in this book require the use of a Thermomix but it does make the entire process a whole lot easier. You no longer need a large number of complicated tools and gadgets to make your own skincare products. The Thermomix takes care of it all. Throw away your kitchen scales, donate the double boiler to charity and give your kitchen whizz to a friend! The Thermomix takes making skincare to a whole new level and it allows anyone who owns one the opportunity to create wholesome, affordable skincare products conveniently at home.

Rich in nutrients, vitamins, antioxidants and full of soul, the products you create for yourself will be superior to any you buy in the store.

The Thermomix can knock up a serum in seconds, blend up balms in minutes and help you to create a beauty bag of delightful items in just hours.

My Story

When people ask me how I got into all this, what influenced my love of creating skincare and what started me on the path to creating my own products, I feel self-conscious telling them how it all began. But the truth is this...

As a very young girl, I would delight for hours, mixing up concoctions of rainwater, leaves, flowers, bark, moss and anything else I could find growing in mum's garden. I would chop, grind, mix and stir until perfectly pulverised and would then proudly present my creation to whoever was about to try. Many years have passed since those innocent play days, my love of the garden has grown into an adoration of nature and my love of concocting mossy colognes has blossomed into a passion for creating luxurious, natural, nourishing skincare. My mums' garden is now a farm growing lavender, rose, chamomile, lemongrass, rosemary, lime and orange which in turn became the organic botanicals used in many of my formulations.

Growing up so close to nature instilled in me an admiration for this incredible planet and with that came a desire to help protect it. I became concerned about the chemical run off that polluted our waterways and how this affected natural species. I began to educate myself about the products I was using.

Alarmed at what I learned and frustrated at not having easy access to natural, safe and ethical alternatives I decided to make my own. I studied, I read, I researched. I tried, I failed and I tried again. I kept at it until I it all came together. My formulas were working! I was creating safe and natural products.

By making my own products I was able to ensure the ingredients I used were non–toxic. I soon began to realise the products I was making felt superior to ones I had been buying. Before I knew it, mine and my family's skin was radiant and our complexions were glowing. We smelt wonderfully sweet, without a whiff of artificial fragrances anywhere. Five years on and with a new found companion in the Thermomix I am on a mission to share what I have learnt. My hope is to inspire TM users, the world over, to make their own sumptuous and safe skincare.

"I suddenly realised that for years and years I had been feeding my skin junk! And not just my skin, my local waterways too! As I researched further, I began to realise that many ingredients in the products I had been buying were laden with chemicals. I learnt, with regular or prolonged use, these ingredients accumulate in our bodies as toxic time bombs."

started

Before blending any of these beauty mixes there are a few fundamentals you need to know. These basics are the building blocks to cosmetic chemistry and are the secret to creating successful formulas. Don't be put off by the mention of chemistry because once you have your head around the basics, these recipes are super easy to make.

Contamination Concerns

Some TM owners may be concerned about cross contamination when using their bowl to make skincare. Some might consider investing in a second bowl. Another bowl would be useful but it is not necessary. Sterlising your bowl and blades before and after use is recommended and a thorough wash (or run through the hottest dishwasher cycle) will usually clean it effectively for whatever you cook up next.

CLEANING YOUR BOWL

Making waxy creams or balms can at first seem daunting especially when it comes to cleaning the bowl. Sometimes the emulsion sets quickly and can leave a waxy coating. Rest assured, the clean-up is not as difficult as it may seem (method below.)

STERILISING YOUR TM

Ensuring your equipment is free from bacteria and microbes is essential. To avoid using harsh or toxic chemicals, I recommend the following method:

Firstly, run your bowl, blades and any tools you will be using through the hottest cycle in your dishwasher.

Next, fill the bowl with water and 2 cups of white vinegar, set TM to **5 minutes/90 degrees/speed 2**, dry thoroughly.

Your bowl is now sanitised.

CLEANING UP AFTER MAKING WAXY FORMULAS

1. Remove as much of the remaining product as you can with a spatula or paper towel.
2. Half fill the bowl with water and add a drop or two of dishwashing liquid.
3. Run **2 minutes/90 degrees/speed 4**.
4. Run again **2 minutes/90 degrees/speed 4 reverse**.
5. Use your TM cleaning brush to loosen any stubborn balm.
6. Pour out (on an inconspicuous spot in the garden) and then wash bowl in hot soapy water. If a waxy residue remains, wipe clean with paper towel.

PRESERVATIVES

Preservatives receive a bad rap much of the time, though they are a vital ingredient and necessary to stabilise formulations and prevent the growth of microbes such as bacteria, mould, yeast and fungi. Microbes are especially fond of water, and so preservatives are an important addition to any skincare recipe that contains water (including hydrosol and floral water.) Some preservatives are thought to be harmful to our bodies, luckily there are safe alternatives available and these are the ones I use and recommend. When choosing a preservative, look for one offering broad-spectrum protection.

For natural formulations, the following are proven as the best and safest.

POTASSIUM SORBATE is a natural preservative that inhibits moulds, fungus and some bacteria. Potassium Sorbate is a water-soluble powder and needs to be added to the waters while heating. It is best used alongside an additional preservative such as phenoxyethanol. Recommended usage levels are between 0.1% to 0.5% when used alone or 0.02% to 0.09% when used in conjunction with another preservative. It is heat stable to 70 degrees.

IMPORTANT: If using potassium sorbate in these recipes you will need to add it to the waters rather than with with essential oils.

PHENOXYETHANOL is a synthetic non-hazardous preservative. It is ideal at inhibiting bacteria and can be used with an additional preservative to ensure your formulations are also effective at preventing the growth of fungus, yeast and mould. Recommended usage levels are between 0.5% to 1% of total volume of the finished product e.g, add between 0.5gram to 1gram of phenoxyethanol for every 100grams of the total volume of ingredients in the batch. It is heat stable up to 85 degrees.

my choice

NATICIDE is derived from natural sources. Not officially classified as a preservative but as a fragrance, it is a broad-spectrum inhibitor of bacteria, mould, yeast and fungi and has a sweet subtle aroma. It is heat stable to 70 degrees, and usage is recommended between 0.3% to 1%. Naticide is approved for use in organic formulations.

EMULSIFIER

Emulsifiers are an essential ingredient in creams and lotions. They are used to bind oil and water molecules together. Without them creams will separate, and the finished product will be a watery, lumpy and messy mixture. Emulsifiers are available in synthetic form or as a plant-based wax. I prefer to use the plant-based products, especially the emulsifier derived from olives.

Floral Waters

Floral waters are also referred to as hydrosols and are highly aromatic. Floral waters can replace the water content in any recipe in this book. Floral waters are a by-product of essential oil production and can be created by steam, or by steeping. Rosewater and Orange Blossom water are readily available at supermarkets, delis and grocery stores, though there are many more varieties available from skincare ingredient suppliers (refer to the list later in this chapter.)

USEFUL BITS & BOBS

- Pyrex jugs (both small and large)
- Silicon Spatula
- Pipettes – used for measuring small amounts of essential oil. Available from most ingredient suppliers.
- Cc scoops – for measuring small amounts of oxides or mica. Available from most ingredient suppliers.
- Sterilising solution such as alcohol wipes, denatured alcohol or surgical spirits.
- Dedicated packaging or recycled (and sterilised) jars and bottles.
- Tags or ready to print labels.

SOLUBILIZER

Just as emulsifiers are used to bind oil and water particles in creams and lotions, solubilzers are used in water based formulas; namely toners and mists, to connect oil and water molecules. They are essential to combine all ingredients and avoid separation in the final product. There are many different types of solubilizers available on the market, and finding the right one can be daunting. For those just starting out, I recommend using **Polysorbate-20** as it is safe, easy to use and affordable.

Essential Oils

Essential oils add so much more to skincare formulations than just a pleasant scent. The therapeutic benefits they offer are diverse and plentiful. Essential oils aid the body in many ways; they enter the body by being absorbed or inhaled and once inside the body the particles circulate through the bloodstream, travelling to various organs and systems to impart their healing value. Particular oils can also offer powerful mental, emotional and psychological support.

FRAGRANCE OIL

Essential oils and fragrance oil are often confused. Fragrance oils are synthetic and can cause adverse skin reactions, especially in people with sensitive skin. I do not recommend using fragrance oil in skincare formulations though they are wonderful for candles and room sprays.

PHOTOSENSITIZATION WARNING

Some essential oils can cause skin photosensitization (a condition that increases the skins sensitivity to the sun.) The following oils are to be avoided in face and body products if sun exposure is likely: **angelica root, bergamot, cumin, grapefruit, cold pressed lemon, lime or orange (distilled varieties are ok) and rue.**

ESSENTIAL OIL SAFETY TIPS

- Pure essential oils are potent and can be harmful if used incorrectly so always use with great care and in minimal quantities.
- Never apply undiluted essential oils directly to the skin. EO's must be diluted in a carrier oil, butter, wax or floral water before applying to the skin.
- Children are more sensitive to EO's, so if preparing a product for children or babies use half the recommended amount of EO (the recipes in the baby chapter of this book have already been adjusted.)
- Some EO's can cause photosensitization when skin is exposed to the sun and in extreme cases can cause a change in skin pigmentation (see warning opposite.)

ESSENTIAL OILS IN PREGNANCY

There are contradictory opinions about the safety of using essential oils while pregnant. To be sure, do your own research. Also, to be safe, avoid using the following essential oils while pregnant or breastfeeding: **aniseed, basil, birch, camphor, hyssop, parsley leaf or seed, pennyroyal, sage, tansy, tarragon, thuja, wintergreen and wormwood.**

Packaging

The type of packaging you require depends on the products you intend to make, your budget, and whether they are for gift giving, resale or your own personal use. Cosmetic packaging comes in all sorts of shapes, colours, materials and designs. If your products are intended as gifts, then you may want to spend a little extra money on new packaging. Though recycled containers, when properly sterilised, will store and keep your handmade creams and lotions just as well. If using recycled packaging, it is imperative that your containers are sterile.

LABELLING

It is good practice to label your products. A label can be simple and handwritten with just the name of the product and the date it was made, or they can be creative and elaborate and include a product name, product description, ingredients list, total volume, expiry date, logo and graphics (this option is nice if you intend to give your products as gifts.) Sheets of labels that can be printed using an inkjet printer can be purchased at office supply stores or for a greater range of colours, shapes and sizes visit www.onlinelabels.com

3 WAYS TO STERLISE RECYCLED JARS

1. Put jars and lids through the hottest cycle of a dishwasher *or* 2. Boil jars and lids in a large pot of water for 20 minutes *or* 3. Place jars (standing upright) on a wooden board & place into the oven on the lowest temperature for 30 minutes.

Sourcing Ingredients

Not all of the ingredients in these recipes are available at the local grocery store, luckily there are many great online suppliers. Before you get started there are two essential ingredients that you will need; at the top of your shopping list will be an emulsifier and a broad spectrum preservative.

Following is a list of suppliers who stock an extensive range of everything you might need.

IN AUSTRALIA

New Directions www.newdirections.com.au

New Directions is a comprehensive stockists and has everything from acids to waxes. They also stock a great range of packaging and will sell in both small and large quantities. New Directions ships throughout Australia and if you are in Sydney, they operate from a huge modern showroom in Marrickville that is open to the public.

Sydney Essential Oil Company www.seoc.com.au

SEOC offers a premium range of essential oils, base oils, extracts, butters and botanicals. The website has many useful resources. Each quarter they publish 'Oily' magazine, which is sent out free to subscribers.

Aussie Soap Supplies www.aussiesoapsupplies.com.au

Aussie Soap Supplies is essentially an online store for soap crafters, but many of the ingredients are useful in other recipes. As well as selling a large range of base ingredients, they also have a great selection of micas and oxides. They have a large range of moulds too.

UNITED STATES

TKB Trading www.tkbtrading.com
TKB Trading has a huge range of micas, oxides and pigments. They also supply a variety of powders and clays. The recipe page on the website is a good resource. They offer fast international shipping.

Making Cosmetics
www.makingcosmetics.com
Making Cosmetics has a comprehensive range of raw ingredients including peptides, proteins and liposomes. International shipping is offered.

Lotion Crafter www.lotioncrafter.com
Lotion Crafter is a wholesale super store, stocking everything from small quantity raw ingredients to equipment for large-scale manufacturing. International shipping is available from their online store, which also has a number of eBooks for sale.

UK/EUROPE

Active Formulas www.activeformulas.com
Active Formulas sells both raw ingredients, including active ingredients and a range of ready to use skincare products.

Gracefruit Limited www.gracefruit.com
Gracefruit stocks a diverse and expanding range of high quality cosmetic ingredients. They ship to all European countries.

Naturally Balmy www.naturallybalmy.co.uk
Naturally Balmy is a family run business specialising in organic ingredients. They also sell kits and packaging, and ship internationally.

Packaging Suppliers

Many of the suppliers above sell a great range of packaging too. Though, there are dedicated packaging suppliers who offer more shapes, sizes, materials, colours and dispensing options. An internet search for cosmetic packaging retailers will yield some firm leads.

This chapter contains recipes for all the body basics. You'll find recipes for lotions, butters and scrubs plus some indulging body treats. All can be mixed up in less than 10 minutes and contain nice, natural ingredients.

LIGHT BODY LOTION

Keep your skin hydrated with this light but penetrating moisturiser. The skin-loving oils in this lotion combine to rehydrate and condition. Use every day for soft supple skin.

330grams Distilled Water (can be replaced with Floral Water of your choice)

75grams Sweet Almond Oil

60grams Light Olive Oil

20grams Emulsifier

7grams Essential Oil*

5grams Vitamin E Oil

5grams Preservative

*Essential Oil – For this lotion I like to use 4grams of jasmine oil, 1 gram pettigrain oil and 2 grams of sweet orange oil.

1. Heat water in TM **3 minutes/80 degrees/speed 3**. Pour into jug and set aside.
2. Measure oils, emulsifier and vitamin E oil into TM and blend **3 minutes/80 degrees/ speed 4**.
3. Add water and blend **30 seconds/speed 4**. Let cool to 50 degrees.
4. Add essential oils and preservative. Mix **10 seconds/ speed 4.**
5. Use a funnel to pour warm lotion into bottles. When completely cool, seal with dispenser.

Application: Apply liberally to entire body daily. For best results apply following a bath or shower.

AVOCADO BODY BUTTER

Bursting with skin moisturising ingredients, the avocado oil in this cream will give skin an intensive boost of pure goodness, plus a big dose of antioxidants.

150grams Rosewater

100grams Avocado Oil

50grams Shea Butter

25grams Emulsifier

5grams Preservative

3grams Geranium Essential Oil

2grams Rose Essential Oil

1. Heat rosewater into TM, **2 minutes/80 degrees/speed 2.** Pour into a small jug and set aside.
2. Measure oil, butter and emulsifier into TM. Mix **2 minutes/80 degrees/speed 3**.
3. Add rosewater and mix **30 seconds/speed 3**. Allow to cool to 50 degrees.
4. Add preservative and essential oil. Mix **10 seconds/ speed 4.**
5. Pour into container. When completely cool seal with lid.

Application: Apply to body after showering or when required.

EVERYDAY BODY MOISTURISER

Whip this body essential up in no time, and your skin will adore you. It absorbs quickly and will leave your skin smooth and hydrated throughout the day. This recipe makes enough for the whole family.

200grams Distilled Water or Aloe Vera Juice

40grams Avocado Oil

40grams Sweet Almond Oil

30grams Grapeseed Oil

30grams Mango Butter

30grams Emulsifier

20grams Shea Butter

5grams Geranium Essential Oil

5grams Preservative

1. Measure water into TM and heat **3 minutes/80 degrees/ speed 1**. Set aside.
2. Measure oils, butters and emulsifier into TM. Mix **3 minutes/80 degrees/speed 4**.
3. Add water and blend **30 seconds/speed 3**. Let cool to 50 degrees.
4. Add essential oils and preservative. Mix **10 seconds/ speed 4**.
5. Pour into container while still warm. Allow to cool completely before sealing with dispenser.

Application: Apply liberally to entire body daily. For best results, apply following a bath or shower.

CUTICLE STICKS

When the skin around your nails grows a little rampant you need to intervene. This natural recipe is just the thing to soften the skin and get your cuticles back into immaculate condition.

20grams Beeswax

10grams Soy Wax

10grams Shea Butter

10grams Mango Butter

20grams Sunflower Oil

5grams Vitamin E Oil

1. Prepare packaging.
2. Measure all ingredients into TM and mix **2 minutes/65 degrees/speed 2.** Scrape down sides of bowl.
3. Blend again **2 minute/65 degrees/speed 1**.
4. Working quickly, use a 5ml syringe to fill tubes. If mixture begins to harden while filling heat the mix **1 minute/60 degrees/speed 0.5**.
5. Allow to cool and then cap.

Application: Apply to the skin around your nails and then with a cuticle stick gently push back the harden skin.

SUGAR & SPICE BODY POLISH

This decadent body scrub will leave your skin soft, sweetly scented and radiant. The brown sugar acts as a gently abrasive and delicately sloughs away dirt, dead skin and impurities. The vanilla improves elasticity and increases circulation while the coconut oil intensively nourishes and restores radiance.

100grams Coconut Oil

50grams Brown Sugar

5grams Cinnamon Powder

5grams Ground Ginger Powder

5grams Ground Nutmeg

5 drops Vanilla Essential Oil

1. Measure all ingredients into TM, mix **15 seconds /speed 5**.
2. Transfer into container.

Application: Rub entirely over wet body in a circular motion, then rinse off in warm water. If using on face, use wet fingertips and gently buff in small circles, avoiding eye area. Rinse.

CLAY & HONEY BODY SCRUB

This scrub is the workhorse of exfoliators and is just the thing for tough, hard or calloused skin. It works wonders on knees, elbows or any place where skin has become thick and rough.

50grams Rice (any variety)

50grams Orange Floral Water (or water)

30grams Kaolin Clay

25grams Honey

1gram Orange Essential Oil

1gram Bergamot Essential Oil

1.Place rice in TM blend **30 seconds/speed 10**. Blend a little longer if you prefer a finer result.

2. Add clay and mix **15 seconds/speed 3.5.**

3. Add remaining ingredients and mix **15 seconds/speed 4.5.**

4.Store in an airtight container and use within 1 week.

Note: This is a coarse exfoliator and not recommended for use on the face.

Application: While showering, massage into required areas in a circular motion and rinse off.

ZESTY BODY SCRUB

This magical body scrub is deep cleansing and will regenerate skin cells, fade blemishes and scars, relieve eczema, dermatitis, psoriasis, acne and heat rash, repair dry, cracked heels, fight cellulite and leave the skin feeling hydrated and adored.

360grams Sea Salt

100grams Apricot Kernel Oil

30grams Jojoba Oil

15 drops Lemon Myrtle Essential Oil

10 drops Lime Essential Oil (distilled is best)

6 drops Eucalyptus Essential Oil

6 drops Rosewood Essential Oil

5 drops Peppermint Essential Oil

4 drops Bergamot Essential Oil

1. Measure all ingredients into TM, **mix 30 seconds/speed 5**.
2. Scoop into containers and seal with lid.

Application: Place about a tablespoon in the palm of your hand. Starting with the upper body, massage gently over your entire body or wherever needed. Rinse off in warm water.

DETOX CLAY BODY WRAP

Show your skin how much you love it with this mineral rich detoxing body mask. Montmorillonite clay is the hero ingredient in this recipe and works to normalise sebum production and draw impurities from the body.

Before you apply the mask, prepare a space where you can lie down and relax. It needs to be somewhere that can be easily cleaned. I like to lay a few old towels on the grass, but a sunlounge would be perfect.

Mask Application: Apply a generous layer to your entire body, but avoid the face and groin area (have a friend or loved one help you apply it to your back.) Wrap your body in an old towel or sarong and leave for as long as possible. Rinse off under a warm shower.

400grams Distilled Water

330grams Green Clay (Montmorillonite)

50grams White Clay

50grams Glycerin

2 Green Tea Bags

3grams Essential Oil *

*I use 1.5grams Lime (distilled), 1gram Juniper berry, and 0.5grams Helichrysum.

1. Steep teabags in 400grams of near boiling water. Set aside to cool a little.
2. Measure clays into TM along with glycerin, essential oils and tea (bags removed.) Mix **30 seconds/speed 4**. Scrape down sides and mix again **30 seconds/speed 4**.
3. Transfer to container.

Wrap Application: After applying the mask, securely wrap your body in bandages; start at your ankles, work up legs, then torso and neck and lastly your arms. Lie back and relax while the minerals get to work (about 30-40 minutes is ideal.) When done, unwrap the bandages and rinse off under a warm shower.

GLIMMERING BODY OIL

Get that healthy bronzed look without exposure to the harsh sun with this golden body oil. The vegetable oils will condition the skin, while the micas will impart a golden hue and a glistening shimmer.

50grams Sweet Almond Oil

35grams Jojoba Oil

25grams Castor Oil

1/4tsp Gold Mica

1/8tsp Aztec Gold Mica

1gram Vitamin E Oil

1gram Frangipani Oil

1gram Jasmine Essential Oil (can be substituted for 1gram of Myrrh Oil)

1. Place all ingredients into TM and blend **10 seconds/speed 5**.
2. Using a funnel transfer into bottle and cap.

Application: Shake very well before each application. Use as much as needed and rub evenly into skin.

CALLUS SCRUB

Gently eliminate tough, unattractive skin patches with this easy to make exfoliator. Bi-carb is a legendary skin-softening agent and will soften stubborn calluses while the salt sloughs away hard skin. The almond oil kindly conditions those rough areas and encourages suppleness. It is perfect to use on ankles, elbows, knees and hands.

50grams Sodium Bicarbonate (Bi-carb Soda)

50grams Table Salt

30grams Almond Oil

20grams Ground Pumice

1gram Lavender Essential Oil

1. Measure dry ingredients into TM and blend **20 seconds/ speed 5**.
2. Scrape down sides of bowl and add oils. Blend **15 seconds/speed 4**.

Application: Use circular motions to apply where needed. Rinse off under warm water. If using in the bath or shower, be careful not to slip.

PEDICURE PASTE

Everyone loves a pedicure, and what better way to prepare your feet for a well-deserved pampering than with this polishing paste. Oatmeal is a star in natural skincare preparations and in this recipe works as a gentle but determined exfoliator. Your feet will be free of flakes, replenished and ready for the finishing touches.

60grams Oatmeal

50grams Table Salt

50grams Almond Oil

15grams Dried Orange Peel (optional)

1gram Sweet Orange Essential Oil (distilled)

1. Measure oatmeal and dried orange peel (if using) into TM and blend **15 seconds/ speed 6**.
2. Add salt and pumice and combine **10 seconds/speed 4**.
3. Add essential oil and mix **5 seconds/speed 5**.
4. Add almond oil and mix **15 seconds/speed 5**.
5. Transfer into an airtight container.

Application: Using your hands, rub in circular motions over the tops, toes, heels, and soles of your feet. Rinse off in warm water, and pat dry with a towel.

DAILY HAND CREAM

Quick to absorb, this lotion will leave your hands hydrated and happy. Avocado oil is intensely nourishing and penetrates deep into the dermal layer to deliver intense hydration at a cellular level.

250grams Distilled Water or Floral Water (I use Ylang Ylang)

65grams Light Olive Oil

50grams Apricot Kernel Oil

50grams Avocado Oil

30grams Beeswax

25grams Jojoba Oil

20grams Emulsifier

5grams Vitamin E Oil

4grams Essential Oil (2 grams each of Mandarin & Bergamot work well)

3grams Preservative

1. Heat waters in TM at **3 minutes/85 degrees/speed 1**. Set aside.
2. Measure oils, emulsifier, wax and vitamin E oil into TM, and blend **4 minutes/80 degrees/ speed 2**.
3. Add waters and mix **30 seconds/speed 3**. Let cool to 50 degrees.
4. Add essential oil and preservative, and mix **10 seconds/speed 3**.
5. Pour into containers and when completely cool, add lids.

Application: Rub into hands morning and night, or as required.

SOOTHING FOOT BALM

Treat your tired or aching feet with this soothing salve. This balm is easily absorbed and will deliver a dose of antioxidant vitamins that will help your feet quickly recover their joie de vivre!

100grams Distilled Water or Floral Water (Eucalyptus works well)

100grams Almond Oil

50grams Wheat Germ Oil

25grams Cocoa Butter

25grams Beeswax

25gram Emulsifier

4grams Preservative

3grams Peppermint Essential Oil

1. Place water in TM and heat **2 minutes/65 degrees/speed 1**. Pour into a heatproof jug and set aside.
2. Measure emulsifier, butter, wax and oil into TM and mix **2 minutes/65 degrees/speed 2**.
3. Add water and blend **20 seconds/speed 6**.Leave to cool to 50 degrees.
4. Add essential oil and preservative. Blend **10 seconds/speed 5**.
5. Pour into containers and when completely cool, secure lid.

Application: Massage into feet and ankles, elevate feet and relax until absorbed.

UPLIFTING MASSAGE OIL

Who doesn't love a massage? Treat your loved ones with this easy-to-make oil that will reinvigorate their senses and uplift their mood.

75grams Grapeseed Oil

25grams Sweet Almond Oil

15grams Evening Primrose Oil

10drops Lemon Myrtle Essential Oil

10 drops Bergamot Essential Oil

8 drops Rosewood Essential Oil

4 drops Eucalyptus Essential Oil

4 drops Rosemary Essential Oil

2 drops Peppermint Essential Oil

1. Measure all ingredients into TM and mix **20 seconds/ speed 3**.
2. Use a funnel to transfer into bottle.

Application: Apply generously to body and massage in with smooth deep strokes.

FLORAL BODY POWDER

This body powder is reminiscent of the rose powder popular at the turn of the 19th century. This old fashioned recipe comes to life with the addition of pink clay and rose otto essential oil.

300grams Corn Starch

150grams Baking Soda

50grams Pink Clay

2grams Rose Otto Essential Oil (or essential oil of your choice)

1. Measure all ingredients into TM and blend **30 seconds/ speed 6.**
2. Spoon into containers.

Application: Apply to dry body (avoid face) after showering.

Face

Put your best face forward by making and using these restorative and supportive formulas. In this chapter you'll find recipes for lotions, serums, toners and polishes that you can whip up for yourself in next to no time.

FACE CLEANSING LOTION

Soothing and calming, this cleansing lotion gently dissolves grime and impurities to leave your skin feeling soft, balanced and fresh.

190grams Distilled Water (or Floral Water of your choice)

50grams Apricot Kernel Oil

20grams Coconut Oil

10grams Emulsifier

5grams Beeswax

2grams Vitamin E Oil

1.5grams Preservative

1.5grams Essential Oil (I use distilled lemon essential oil)

1. Measure waters into bowl and heat **3 minutes/85 degrees/speed 3**. Pour into a jug and set aside.
2. Measure oils, wax and emulsifier into TM and mix **3 minutes/80 degrees/speed 3**.
3. Add waters to oil and mix **30 seconds/speed 4**.
4. Allow to cool to 50 degrees. Add preservative and essential oils and mix **30 seconds/ speed 4**.
5. While warm pour into bottles, and then leave to completely cool before sealing with dispenser or lid.

Application: Apply ½ to 1 teaspoon to your face, neck and décolletage. Gently wipe away with a soft wet washcloth.

FACE PRIMER

Light and hydrating, this moisturising lotion will plump and prime your skin and is perfect for wearing under makeup.

340grams Aloe Vera Juice

70grams Jojoba Oil

65grams Sweet Almond Oil

35grams Emulsifier

15grams Avocado Oil

15grams Apricot Kernel Oil

5grams Preservative

3grams Essential Oil (I like Rose Geranium for this recipe)

2grams Grapefruit Seed Extract (optional)

1. Heat aloe vera juice in TM **3 minutes/80 degrees/speed 2**. Pour into a jug and set aside.
2. Measure oils and emulsifier into TM and mix **3 minutes/80 degrees/speed 2**.
3. Add aloe vera juice to oils and mix **30 seconds/speed 4**.
4. When cooled to 50 degrees, add essential oils and preservative. Blend **30 seconds/speed 4**.
5. Pour into bottles while still warm, leave to cool completely before adding the dispenser or cap.

Application: Apply a small amount and gently massage into your face and neck prior to makeup application.

FACE TONING SPRITZ

Gentle but effective, this toning mist is anti-inflammatory, reduces pore size and leaves skin feeling clean and fresh. This refreshing toner rebalances your skin's subtle pH. It also makes a refreshing face spritz after a workout or in hot, humid weather.

100grams Distilled Water

100grams Jasmine Floral Water

25grams Witch Hazel

15grams Solubilizer

2grams Preservative

2grams Vitamin E Oil

2grams Grapefruit Essential Oil

1gram Sweet Orange Essential Oil

1gram Cedarwood Essential Oil

1gram Clary Sage Essential Oil

1gram Grapefruit Seed Extract

1. Measure waters and witch hazel into TM and blend **10 seconds/speed 4**. Pour into a jug and set aside.
2. Place essential oils, preservative, vitamin E oil, grapefruit seed extract and solubilizer into TM and blend **10 seconds/speed 2**.
3. Add waters and blend **15 seconds/speed 2**.
4. Use a funnel to fill bottles and add cap.

Application: Shake well before using. Use after cleansing, close eyes and mist over entire face and neck. Using a soft cotton pad, gently wipe off. To use throughout the day as a refresher, simply close eyes and mist over entire face and neck.

REFRESHING FACE MIST

Keep your face cool with this specially formulated face spritz. The ingredients work in synergy to tone skin, reduce pore size, equalize oil production and balance pH.

INGREDIENTS

220grams Neroli Floral Water

200grams Distilled Water

50grams Witch Hazel

10grams Glycerin

5grams Solubilizer

4grams Preservative

4grams Grapefruit Seed Extract

3grams Cedarwood Atlas Essential Oil

2grams Sweet Orange Essential Oil (distilled)

2grams Clary Sage Essential Oil

METHOD

1. Measure waters, witch hazel, glycerin and solubilizer into TM and blend **30 seconds/ speed 3**.

2. Add essential oils, preservative and extract, then mix **10 seconds/speed 4**.

3. Use a funnel to pour into containers.

Application: Shake well before using. Mist onto face, neck and décolletage. Can be used as a toner after cleansing and before moisturising or as a refresher throughout the day.

MAKEUP REMOVER

Remove the day's makeup without stripping your skin of moisture with this natural lotion. Your skin will be left feeling clean and fresh.

150grams Floral Water (I like Rosewater)

50grams Aloe Vera Juice

50grams Distilled Water

20grams Jojoba Oil

20grams Coconut Oil

15grams Olive Leaf Extract

10grams Glycerin

10grams Emulsifier

5grams Vitamin E Oil

2grams Xanthan Gum

2grams Preservative

Application: Apply a small amount to cotton pad and wipe over face and eyes.

1. In a small bowl or jug, hydrate xanthan gum by sprinkling it onto warm water and briskly whisking. Set aside.

2. Heat floral water and aloe vera juice in TM **3 minutes/80 degrees/speed 4**. With 1 minute to go, add xanthan mixture. Set aside.

3. Heat oils, extract, emulsifier and vitamin E oil in TM for **2 minutes/80 degrees/speed 4**.

4. Add water mixture and blend **30 seconds/speed 3**. Allow to cool to 50 degrees.

5. Add preservative and mix **10 seconds/speed 3.**

6. Transfer into container and when completely cool, add cap.

VIBRANT FACE SERUM

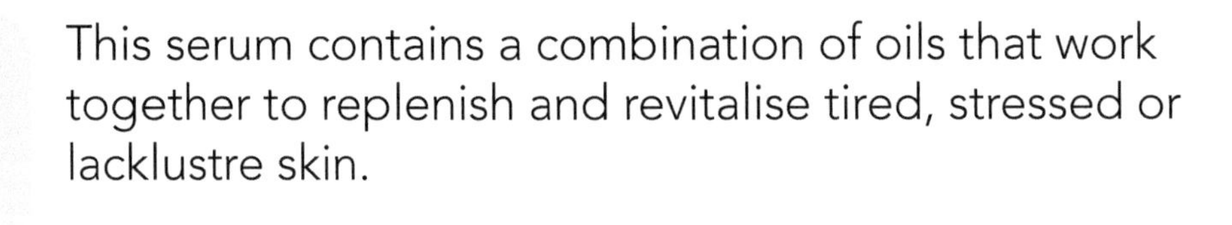

This serum contains a combination of oils that work together to replenish and revitalise tired, stressed or lacklustre skin.

INGREDIENTS

20grams Jojoba Oil

15grams Hazelnut Oil

10grams Rosehip Oil

5grams Vitamin E Oil

6 drops Ylang Ylang Essential Oil

3 drops Cedarwood Essential Oil

3 drops Lavender Essential Oil

METHOD

1. Measure all ingredients into TM and mix **10 seconds/ speed 4.**

2. Using a funnel, pour into container and seal with lid.

Application: After cleansing, apply to damp skin morning and night.

HEALING FACE SERUM

Full of skin-supporting fatty acids, this serum is regenerative and anti-inflammatory. It is perfect for environmentally stressed and mature skin; it can also be used to speed post-operative healing or to help prevent stretch marks.

20grams Rosehip Oil

20grams Hazelnut Oil

10grams Jojoba Oil

10grams Macadamia Oil

3 drops Helichrysum Essential Oil

2 drops Carrot Seed Oil

1. Measure all ingredients into TM and blend **10 seconds/ speed 4**.
2. Using a funnel, pour into container and seal with lid.

Application: Apply to clean, damp skin morning and night.

NIGHT CREAM

Packed full of supportive ingredients, this cream is perfect for nourishing dry or mature skin. It brings incredible healing benefits and delivers a powerful dose of essential fatty acids and vitamins, important for regenerating damaged skin tissues, repairing scarring and reducing wrinkles. Deeply penetrating, avocado oil reduces age spots and promotes skin renewal.

150grams Aloe Vera Juice

50grams Apricot Kernel Oil

30grams Sweet Almond Oil

25grams Avocado Oil

25grams Jojoba Oil

20grams Macadamia Oil

20grams Emulsifier

10grams Rosehip Oil

5grams Vitamin E Oil

3grams Preservative

2grams Essential Oil*

* I use 1gram of Jasmine and 1gram of Lemon (distilled)

1. Heat aloe vera juice in TM **3 minutes/80 degrees/speed 3**. Pour into a jug and set aside.

2. Measure oils, emulsifier and vitamin E oil into TM bowl and blend **3 minutes/80 degrees/speed 3**.

3. Add aloe vera juice and blend **30 seconds/speed 4**. Leave to cool.

4. When temperature drops to 50 degrees, add essential oil and preservative and blend **30 seconds/speed 3**.

5. While the cream is still warm, pour into jars and allow to cool completely before sealing with lid.

Application: Apply to face and neck after cleansing and toning. Use at night for an intensive treatment for normal skin, or use day and night for dry or mature skin.

REJUVENATING FACE PEEL

This mask is a perfect pick-me-up for tired or surly skin. Pink clay will cleanse, refresh and detoxify, while the jojoba oil works to restore moisture.

40grams Aloe Vera Juice

30grams Distilled Water

10grams Gelatine

5grams Jojoba Oil

5grams Pink Argiletz Clay

4 drops Rose Otto Essential Oil

2 drops Helichrysum Essential Oil

1. Heat water and aloe vera juice in TM for **2 minutes/85 degrees/speed 0.5**.
2. Sprinkle gelatine over the water and blend for **15 seconds/speed 7**.
3. Add jojoba oil and clay and mix **15 seconds/speed 6**.
4. Allow to cool to 30 degrees before applying.

Application: Apply to face, neck and décolletage, taking care to avoid the eyes, allow to dry. Wash off with warm water.

ROSE FACE POLISH

A smooth and bright complexion is assured with this generous exfoliate. Containing a host of superstar ingredients bestowed on us by Mother Nature herself, this polish will reveal the goddess within.

75grams Rosewater

40grams Almond Meal

30grams Oatmeal

25grams Walnut Shell (ground)

25grams Pink Clay

25grams White Clay (or Kaolin)

25grams Rose Petal Powder

3grams Essential Oil (I like Rose Otto for this recipe)

2grams Preservative

1. Place oatmeal into TM and process **10 seconds/speed 5**.
2. Add almond meal, rose petal powder, clays and mix **45 seconds/speed 4**. Scrape the sides of bowl and then blend again **20 seconds/speed 3**.
3. Measure rosewater into bowl. Add the preservative and mix **30 seconds/speed 3**.
4. Add ground walnut shell and mix **30 seconds/speed 3**.
5. Scoop into container and seal.

Application: In circular motions apply to face, neck and décolletage. Rinse off with warm water.

SOOTHING CLAY MASK

Overflowing with a multitude of heavenly goodness, this mask will deliver a powerful dose of vitamins, minerals and antioxidants that will soothe and repair your skin and reinvigorate your complexion.

Application: Apply a generous layer to your face, neck and décolletage, paying careful attention to avoid eyes. It can also be applied as an all over body mask. After 15-20 minutes, rinse off with warm water.

200grams Aloe Vera Juice

100grams Hazelnut Oil

50grams Macadamia Oil

25grams Yellow Clay

25grams Shea Butter

25grams Cetyl Alcohol

5grams Vitamin E Oil

3grams Preservative

3grams Essential Oil*

2.5grams Xanthan Gum

*I use Vetiver essential oil for its anti-inflammatory, healing and calming properties.

1. Place aloe vera juice in TM and heat **1 minute/ 90 degrees/speed 2**.
2. Add xanthan gum and mix **30 seconds/speed 3.5**. Set aside and rinse bowl.
3. Measure oils, butter and cetyl alcohol into TM and blend **1 minute/80 degrees/speed 3.5**.
4. Set TM for **1 minute/speed 3** and slowly add the aloe vera mix.
5. Add clay and mix **1 minute/ speed 3**.
6. When cooled to 50 degrees, add preservative and essential oil and blend **30 seconds/speed 4**.
7. Pour into pots and allow to cool before putting lids on.

CITRUS & CLOVE FACE SCRUB

While this scrub is formulated with masculine accents, it lovingly nurtures all skin types. This face exfoliant is tender but effective.

40grams Oatmeal

25grams Sweet Almond Oil

10grams Ground Walnut Shell

10grams Brown Sugar

2grams Preservative

2 drops Clove Essential Oil

2 drops Tangerine Essential Oil

1. Place oatmeal in TM and grind for **10 seconds/speed 7.**
2. Add all other ingredients and blend **10 seconds/speed 7**.
3. Transfer to jar and secure lid tightly.

Application: Using your fingertips, apply to face and neck in small circular motions. Rinse off with warm water.

ROSEHIP EYE CREAM

The skin around our eyes is delicate and as we age this skin tends to get thinner. Nurture this area with a gentle dose of antioxidants and amino acids found in this specially formulated recipe.

60grams Distilled Water

25grams Rosehip Oil

25gram Jojoba Oil

10grams Emulsifier

3grams Essential Oil (Rose Otto is perfect for this recipe)

1gram Preservative

1. Measure water into TM and heat **2 minutes/85 degrees/ speed 2**. Set aside.
2. Measure oils and emulsifier into TM and mix **2 minutes/ 80 degrees/speed 2**.
3. Turn TM to **1 minute/speed 4** and slowly add water. Let cool to 50 degrees.
4. Add preservative and essential oil and mix **30 seconds/speed 4**.
5. Pour into containers and when completely cool seal with lid.

Application: Gently dab a small amount around eyes and then carefully blend into skin. Use morning and night.

LUSH LIP BALM

Pucker up with this sumptuous balm. The all-natural ingredients will nourish and protect your lips and impart a glossy sheen.

20grams Grapeseed Oil

20grams Almond Oil

20grams Soy Wax

20grams Shea Butter

15grams Beeswax

10grams Jojoba Oil

10grams Essential Oil (I like Mandarin for this recipe)

1. Measure all ingredients (except essential oil) into TM and blend **3 minutes/65 degrees/speed 2**. If a few pieces of unmelted wax or butter remain, blend again at 65 degrees until all melted. Let cool to 50 degrees.

2. Add essential oil and mix **10 seconds/speed 2.**

3. Pour into containers and allow to set before capping.

NATURAL LIP TINT

Bursting with natural waxes and organic plant oils, these lip tints will give a subtle hint of colour and keep your lips perky, soft and nourished.

30grams Coconut Oil

20grams Almond Oil

10grams Jojoba Oil

10grams Beeswax

5grams Soy Wax

5grams Carnauba Wax

1/2tsp Mica pigment (colour of your choice)*

1. Prepare packaging.
2. Measure oils and waxes into TM and blend **4 minutes/65 degrees/speed 2.**
3. Add pigment and mix **10 seconds/speed 3.**
4. Working quickly, use the syringe to fill your tubes or containers. Leave to set.

**WARNING:* Use only lip safe micas and pigments.*

NOTE: When using tubes there is a chance the balms will develop sinkholes as they harden. This is easily fixed by adding a few drops of the hot balm blend as they cool and harden.

GUY'S FACE LOTION

MAKES: 340grams
TIME: 10 minutes
PACKAGING: Glass or plastic bottle with pump cap. Use within 6 months.

This one is for the boys and even though not every man appreciates the benefits of moisturising, after using this lotion their skin will sing its praises. Grapeseed oil and meadowfoam seed oil are especially noble additions to this lotion and work together to smooth, calm and detoxify.

INGREDIENTS

210grams Aloe Vera Juice

30grams Avocado Oil

30grams Grapeseed Oil

20grams Sweet Almond Oil

20grams Meadowfoam Seed Oil

20grams Emulsifier

6grams Essential Oil*

4grams Preservative

*I use 2grams of Clove and 2grams of Mandarin for this recipe.

METHOD

1. Heat aloe vera juice in TM at **3 minutes/85 degrees/speed 2**. Pour into a jug and set aside.
2. Measure oils and emulsifier into TM. Mix **3 minutes/80 degrees/speed 3.**
3. Pour aloe vera into oils and blend **30 seconds/speed 4**.
4. When mix has cooled to 50 degrees, add the essential oils and preservative. Blend **30 seconds/speed 4.**
5. While warm, pour into bottles. Wait until lotion is completely cool before capping.

Application: Apply to clean dry skin.

AFTER SHAVE SPRAY

This natural aftershave formulation is just what your man needs to reduce skin irritation and prevent infection after shaving. The essential oils used give this lotion a subtle citrus aroma.

150grams Witch Hazel

50grams Vodka

20grams Glycerin

5grams Solubilizer

2grams Lime Essential Oil (distilled)

1gram Sweet Orange Essential Oil (distilled)

1gram Cinnamon Essential Oil

1gram Mint Essential Oil

1. Measure all ingredients into TM and mix **20 seconds/ speed 6**.
2. Use a funnel to pour into container.

Application: Mist onto freshly shaved skin. Avoid eyes.

natural Remedies

With a few special ingredients and the recipes in this chapter your medicine cupboard will be full of wholesome natural remedies.

ALOE HAND SANITISER

MAKES: 200grams

TIME: 5 minutes

PACKAGING: Bottle with pump dispenser.

Use within 6 months.

Destroy dangerous germs naturally with this natural homemade sanitiser. The ingredients it contains are unfavourable to bacteria but kind to skin.

INGREDIENTS

100grams Aloe Vera Gel

90grams Witch hazel

20grams Vodka

5grams Vitamin E Oil*

*NOTE: For a clear gel omit the Vitamin E oil.

METHOD

1. Measure all ingredients into bowl and mix on **30 seconds/ speed 3 reverse**.
2. Scrape down sides of bowl with spatula and mix again on **30 seconds/speed 3 reverse**.
3. Transfer to containers.

Application: Apply to hands and rub in. Use as required.

AFTER SUN MIST

MAKES: 200grams

TIME: 5 minutes

PACKAGING: Plastic bottle with atomiser.

Use within 2 months.

Sunburn isn't fun for anyone. Enjoy quick relief with this simple to make, soothing mist.

INGREDIENTS

2 Green Tea Bags

100grams Distilled Water

60grams Aloe Vera Juice

30grams Glycerin

10grams Solubilizer

2grams Preservative

0.5grams Lavender Essential Oil

0.5grams Chamomile Essential Oil

METHOD

1. Steep teabags in 100grams of boiling water for about 15 minutes. Remove teabags and set aside to cool.
2. Add water, aloe vera juice and glycerin to TM and mix **10 seconds/speed 3.** Pour into a jug and set aside.
3. Add oils and solubilizer to TM and mix **10 seconds/speed 2.5**.
4. Add waters and mix **15 seconds/speed 2**.
5. Use a funnel to fill bottles and cap.

Application: Mist over sunburned skin as required. Store in the fridge for some extra cool relief.

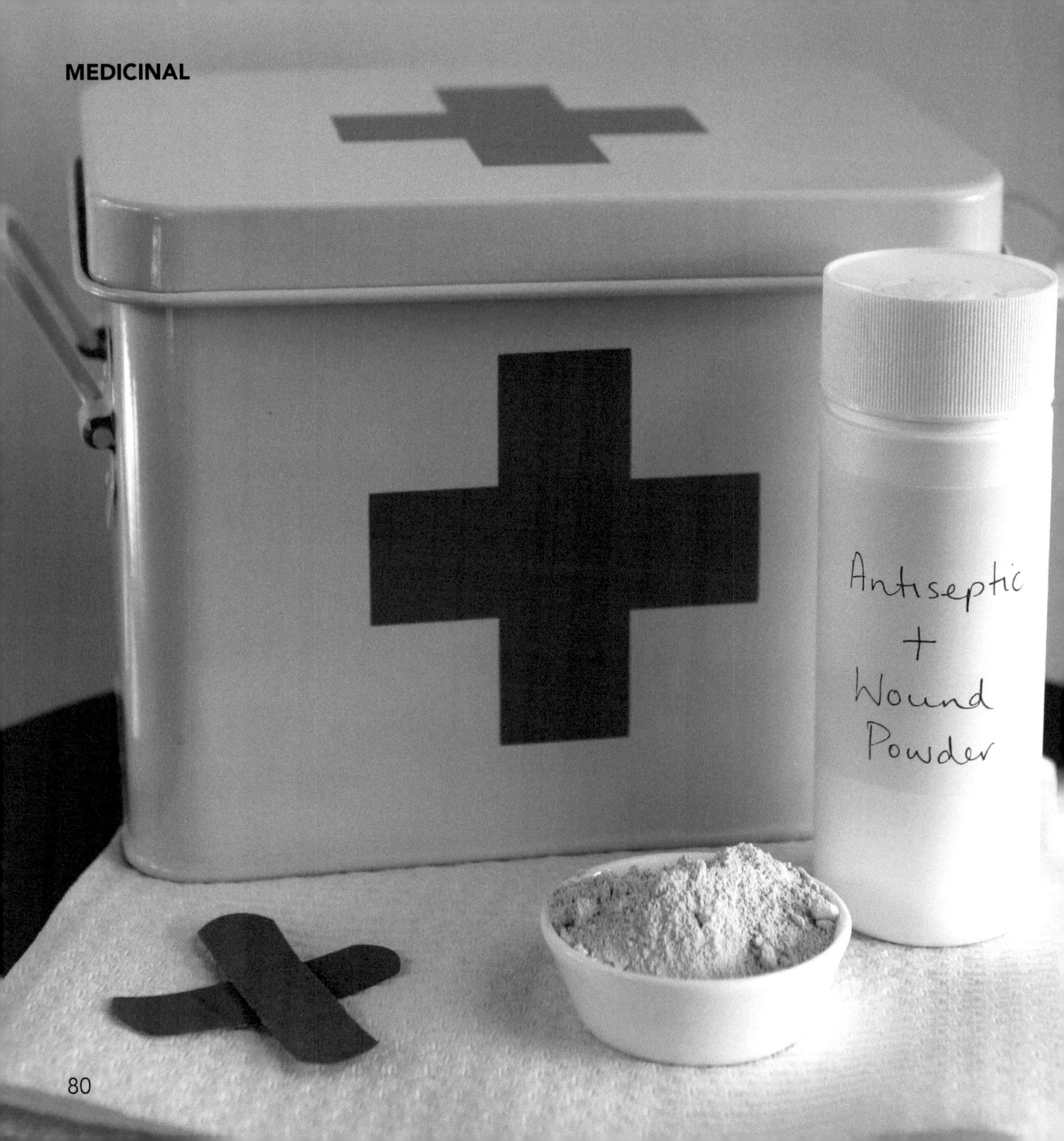
Antiseptic
+
Wound
Powder

ANTISEPTIC WOUND POWDER

MAKES: 100grams

TIME: 5 minutes

PACKAGING: Plastic or cardboard powder dispenser.

Use within 9 months.

The healing power of pepper is a little known secret. For centuries, pepper was an established cure for minor cuts and wounds. Pepper disinfects, encourages coagulation and supports scab creation. It also helps the wounds to heal faster and reduces the chances of scarring. If you have doubts, I urge you to try it for yourself.

INGREDIENTS

30grams Finely Ground Pepper (Black or White)*

40grams Kaolin Clay

40grams Zinc Oxide

*NOTE: If need be, you can use your Thermomix to grind the pepper. Simply measure the required amount of peppercorns into your TM and mix 15 seconds/speed 9. Continue with these settings until the pepper is at the desired consistency.

METHOD

1. Measure all ingredients into TM bowl and mix **10 seconds/ speed 5**.
2. Store in an airtight container.

Application: When required, cover wound completely with powder and if necessary cover with a dressing. For deep cuts, serious wounds and heavy bleeding, always consult a doctor.

CRACKED FEET BALM

MAKES: 165grams

TIME: 10 minutes

PACKAGING: Plastic or glass jar with screw top lid.

Use within 6 months.

You will never have to worry about unsightly feet again. Regular use of this balm will soften and condition hard, dry, cracked skin and have you putting your best feet forward. The lanolin in this recipe doubles as both a moisturiser and protective agent, and will penetrate and soften tough skin from within. This recipe also works wonders on elbows, knees and ankles.

INGREDIENTS

60grams Eucalyptus Floral Water (or Distilled Water)

30grams Sweet Almond Oil

20grams Apricot Kernel Oil

10grams Castor Oil

10grams Lanolin

10grams Emulsifier

10grams Shea Butter

10grams Beeswax

2grams Preservative

1gram Rosemary Essential Oil

1gram Eucalyptus Essential Oil

METHOD

1. Heat water in TM heat for **4 minutes/75 degrees/speed 1**. Set aside.

2. Measure oils, wax, butter, lanolin and emulsifier in TM and mix **3 minutes/75 degrees/ speed 1**.

3. Add water and blend **30 seconds/speed 3**. Leave to cool to 50 degrees.

4. Add essential oils and preservative, blend **15 seconds/speed 4**.

5. Pour into containers and when completely cool, add lid.

Application: Rub into cracked, dry or callused skin morning and night.

BLEMISH GEL

MAKES: 120grams

TIME: 5 minutes

PACKAGING: Airtight Container.

Use within 2 months.

This antibacterial infusion of oils and extracts will help to heal and soothe acne and blemishes. All ingredients are derived from natural sources, so it is safe and effective.

INGREDIENTS

100grams Aloe Vera Gel

10grams Chamomile Floral Water

5grams Vitamin E Oil

1gram Grapefruit Seed Extract

1gram Rosemary Essential Oil

1gram Lavender Oil

METHOD

1. Measure all ingredients into TM and mix **45 seconds/ speed 4**.
2. Scrape down sides and blend again **30 seconds/speed 1**.
3. Transfer into container.

Application: With clean hands, dab a small amount onto affected area and gently massage in. Use as required.

VAPOUR BALM

MAKES: 200grams

TIME: 10 minutes

PACKAGING: Wide jar with screw top lid.

Use within 6 months.

Chase away that blah feeling and relieve congestion, inflammation and stuffiness with this all-natural balm. Unlike traditional, store bought products it contains no petroleum, so it is perfectly safe to use on the little ones.

INGREDIENTS

75grams Shea Butter

40grams Coconut Oil

30grams Apricot Kernel Oil

25grams Beeswax (can be substituted with Candelilla Wax)

20grams Menthol Crystals*

3grams Eucalyptus Oil

1gram Tea Tree Oil

*If you prefer a stronger balm, increase Menthol Crystals to 40grams but be prepared for a robust vapcur and watery eyes.

METHOD

1. Measure butter, oils and wax into TM bowl and mix **3 minutes/65 degrees/speed 4**.
2. Add menthol crystals to melted oil mix and blend **2 minutes/65 degrees/speed 2**.
3. When cooled to 50 degrees add essential oils and blend **15 seconds/speed 4.**

Application: Gently rub onto chest, wrists, temples and behind ears when required. It can also be applied to a tissue and inhaled as required.

HEADACHE BALM

MAKES: 85grams

TIME: 10 minutes

PACKAGING: Small jar with airtight lid.

Use within 6 months.

For a natural alternative to headache relief, try this simple salve. The essential oils combine to naturally relieve emotional tension and bodily stress.

INGREDIENTS

50grams Extra Virgin Olive Oil

25grams Castor Oil

10grams Beeswax

1.5grams Sweet Orange Essential Oil

1gram Grapefruit Essential Oil

0.5grams Marjoram Essential Oil

0.5grams Ginger Essential Oil

0.5grams Rosemary Essential Oil

0.5grams Lavender Essential Oil

METHOD

1. Measure oils and beeswax into TM and heat **3 minutes/65 degrees/speed 3.**
2. When cooled to 50 degrees, add essential oils and mix **10 seconds/speed 3.**
3. Pour into containers and when completely cool, secure lid.

Application: Using your fingertips, gently massage into temples and pressure points.

NATURAL INSECT REPELLENT

MAKES: 380grams

TIME: 5 minutes

PACKAGING: Plastic bottle with an atomiser.

Use within 6 months.

Conventional store bought insect repellents are teeming with toxic ingredients, some of which are proven carcinogens. Do yourself and your loved ones a favour and try this natural alternative instead.

INGREDIENTS

250grams Lavender Floral Water

100grams Witch Hazel

20grams Glycerin

3grams Citronella Essential Oil

2grams Peppermint Essential Oil

2grams Lavender Essential Oil

1gram Eucalyptus Essential Oil

1gram Rosemary Essential Oil

1gram Thyme Essential Oil

METHOD

1. Place all ingredients in TM and mix **30 seconds/speed 7**.
2. Using a funnel, pour into bottles and cap.
3. Shake well before use.

Application: Mist over exposed skin. Repeat as required.

NATURAL SUN BLOCK

MAKES: 410 grams

TIMES: 10 minutes

PACKAGING: Pump Bottle

Use within 6 months

This sun block is much the same as the old fashion zinc cream widely available in the 1970's and 1980's. It contains natural oils and butters to hydrate skin and zinc oxide to protect the skin from UV rays.

INGREDIENTS

150grams Distilled Water

90grams Coconut Oil

70grams Sunflower Oil

55grams Zinc Oxide (will give a S.P.F of 20)

25grams Shea Butter

15grams Emulsifier

5grams Vitamin E Oil

3grams Preservative

METHOD

1. Measure water in TM and heat **2 minutes/80 degrees/ speed 1**. Set aside.

2. Measure oils, butter and emulsifier in TM and mix **3 minutes/80 degrees/speed 3**.

3. Add water to TM and mix **1 minutes/speed 4**.

4. Add zinc oxide and blend **2 minutes/speed 3**. Allow to cool to 50 degrees.

5. Add preservative and mix **5 seconds/speed 3**.

6. Use a funnel to transfer into container. When completely cool secure lid.

Application: Apply to exposed skin prior to heading outdoors. Reapply every 2 hours or after swimming.

NATURAL MINTY TOOTHPASTE

MAKES: 420grams

TIME: 10 minutes

PACKAGING: Squeeze tube is ideal; otherwise store in an airtight container.

If you are used to foamy, sweet toothpaste, this one may take a little getting used to. Though if you can get past these omissions, you will be rewarded with a healthy and affordable natural alternative.

INGREDIENTS

200grams Distilled Water

100grams Sodium Bicarbonate

50grams Glycerin

50grams Calcium Carbonate

10grams Silica

10grams Stevia

1/4tsp Xanthan Gum

1/4tsp Menthol Crystals

4 drops Peppermint Essential Oil

2 drops Eucalyptus Essential Oil

2 drops Fennel Essential Oil

METHOD

1. Place 1 tablespoon of warm water into a small bowl. Add xanthan gum and whisk into a paste. Stir this mix into ¼ cup of warm water, set aside.
2. Place glycerin into TM, heat **1 minute/50 degrees/speed 1**.
3. Add menthol crystals and combine **2 minutes/50degrees/speed 2**. Menthol crystals will dissolve.
4. Add baking soda, silica, calcium carbonate, stevia and water to glycerin blend, mix **20 seconds/speed 4**.
5. Add xanthan mix, blend **1 minute/50 degrees/speed 4**.
6. Scrape down side of bowl and add essentials oils. Mix **30 seconds/speed 2**. Transfer into container.

THERAPEUTIC LIP BALM

MAKES: 100grams

TIME: 10 minutes

PACKAGING: Small jars with airtight lids.

Use within 4 months.

Give sore lips some relief with this calming balm. It is easy to make and will alleviate painful lips in seconds. Coconut and avocado oils work together to nourish, while the honey mends and protects.

INGREDIENTS

50grams Avocado Oil

30grams Coconut Oil

10grams Beeswax

5grams Honey

5grams Vitamin E Oil

1gram Peppermint Oil

METHOD

1. Measure all ingredients into TM and blend **4 minutes/65 degrees/speed 1.5** or until all waxes have melted.
2. Add essential oil and blend **10 seconds/speed 1.5**.
3. Pour into containers and leave to cool. When completely cool, add lids.

Application: Apply liberally to lips when required.

SLEEP BALM

MAKES: 175grams

TIME: 10 minutes

PACKAGING: Small plastic or aluminium pots.

Use within 4 months.

Fight insomnia the natural way. The essential oils in this balm will assist in relaxing the senses and lull you into a blissful slumber. It will also benefit hyperactive or overexcited kids at bedtime.

INGREDIENTS

100grams Soybean Oil

25grams Beeswax

25grams Mango Butter

25grams Shea Butter

1.5grams Sweet Orange Essential Oil

1gram Geranium Essential Oil

1gram Lavender Essential Oil

0.5grams Vanilla Essential Oil

METHOD

1. Measure oils, butters and beeswax into TM and heat **4 minutes/65 degrees/speed 1**. Butters and waxes should be melted.
2. Leave to cool. When cooled to 50 degrees, add essential oils and blend **10 seconds/ speed 3**.
3. Pour into containers and when completely cool, secure lid.

Application: Use your fingertips to gently massage into temples, behind ears and wrists.

CONDITIONING LIP BALM

MAKES: 55grams

TIME: 10 minutes

PACKAGING: Small jars with airtight lids.

Use within 4 months.

Brimming with therapeutic oils and butters, this balm will take the sting out of painful or aggravated lips and help heal chaffed skin.

INGREDIENTS

10grams Soy Wax

10grams Shea Butter

10grams Grapeseed Oil

10grams Sweet Almond Oil

10grams Jojoba Oil

5grams Beeswax

10 drops Peppermint Essential Oil

4 drops Rosemary Essential Oil

METHOD

1. Measure waxes, oils and butters into TM and mix **4 minutes/65 degrees/ speed 1.5** (or until all waxes have melted.)

2. Add essential oil and mix **5 seconds/speed 2.**

3. Pour into prepared containers and when completely cool, add lids.

Application: Apply to dry, sore or chapped lips as required.

oh baby

Ensure your baby's body stays pure with these non-toxic products.
Made with all natural ingredients and absolutely no nasties you
can manage what goes into their little bodies right from the start.

BABY BUM BALM

MAKES: 360grams
TIME: 15 minutes
PACKAGING: Wide mouth jar with airtight lid.
Use within 6 months.

This balm glides easily onto babies' skin, making it sympathetic to irritated skin and rashes. The ingredients are all natural and safe for delicate skin.

INGREDIENTS

100grams Aloe Vera Juice

100grams Shea Butter

70grams Coconut Oil

50grams Avocado Oil

20grams Beeswax

15grams Emulsifier

5grams Vitamin E Oil

3grams Preservative

1gram Chamomile Essential Oil (optional)

METHOD

1. Measure aloe vera juice into TM **3 minutes/65 degrees/ speed 1**. Set aside.
2. Place oils, butter and emulsifier in TM **4 minutes/65 degrees/speed 4**.
3. Pour aloe vera juice into TM and blend **1 minute/speed 4**. Let cool to 50 degrees.
4. Add essential oil and preservative and mix **30 seconds/speed 4**.
5. While warm, pour into container and let cool completely before capping.

Application: Gently apply to clean, dry skin after nappy change or when needed.

BEAUTIFUL BABY LOTION

MAKES: 270grams

TIME: 10 minutes

PACKAGING: Plastic bottle with pump dispenser.

Use within 6 months.

Babies are born with lovely supple skin but even so, their skin benefits from regular care and nourishment. This lotion is formulated with gentle yet caring ingredients that will help keep young skin soft and conditioned.

INGREDIENTS

100grams Aloe Vera Juice

70grams Chamomile Floral Water

50grams Sunflower Oil

30grams Aloe Vera Gel

10grams Emulsifier

5grams Cocoa Butter

5grams Preservative

METHOD

1. Measure aloe vera juice, floral water and gel into TM and mix **2 minutes/90 degrees/ speed 2 reverse**. Pour into a jug and set aside.

2. Place oil and butter into TM and blend **2 minutes/90 degrees/speed 5**.

3. Add aloe and water mix to oils and blend **30 seconds/ speed 4**. Let cool to 50 degrees.

4. Add preservative. **Mix 30 seconds/speed 4**.

5. Using a funnel transfer to bottles. When completely cool,

Application: Gently massage into baby's skin after bath time or before dressing.

PREGNANT BELLY BALM

MAKES: 100grams

TIME: 10 minutes

PACKAGING: Aluminium or plastic pot with airtight lid.

Use within 3 months.

This soothing balm is an idyllic moisturising treatment during pregnancy. It will promote elasticity and soften the skin to minimise stretch marks.

INGREDIENTS

30grams Sweet Almond Oil

15grams Evening Primrose Oil

15grams Avocado Oil

10grams Mango Butter

10grams Shea Butter

10grams Cocoa Butter

5grams Candelilla Wax

5grams Beeswax

3grams Essential Oil (I use 1gram Lavender and 2grams distilled Lemon Oil)

METHOD

1. Measure waxes and oils into TM. Mix for **2 minutes/65 degrees/speed 1 reverse**. Waxes and butters should be melted but if not, mix for another **2 minutes/65 degrees/speed 1 reverse**.
2. Blend **10 seconds/speed 2** to combine.
3. Let cool to 50 degrees and add essential oil. Mix **5 seconds/speed 3**.
4. Pour into prepared packaging and allow to cool completely before adding lid.

Application: Massage into taut skin morning or night.

SOOTHING BABY POWDER

MAKES: 250grams

TIME: 5 minutes

PACKAGING: Plastic or cardboard powder dispenser.

Use within 9 months.

This baby powder contains natural and inert ingredients that are gentle and kind. The addition of chamomile essential oil will help lull baby into a relaxed, calm mood.

INGREDIENTS

50grams Kaolin Clay

50grams Bentonite Clay

50grams Arrowroot Powder

50grams Cornstarch

50grams Zinc Oxide

1gram Chamomile Oil (optional)

METHOD

1. Measure all ingredients into TM and blend **15 seconds/ speed 5**.
2. Remove bowl and gently tap on the palm of your hand to dislodge powder, scrape down sides.
3. Blend again **15 seconds/ speed 5**.
4. Store in an airtight container and use as required.

Application: Apply a light dusting to clean dry skin, after bath or nappy changes.

Healthy *hair*

Hair care products are easily some of the most toxic things we put on our bodies. The recipes in this chapter offer safer alternatives to store bought products. They are effective and affordable too!

HAIR RESCUE SERUM

MAKES: 50grams

TIME: 5 minutes

PACKAGING: Small dark glass bottle.

Use within 4 weeks.

Sun, stress, unhealthy diet and chemical colouring can all take their toll on the health of our hair. Encourage repair and rejuvenation with this serious serum. You'll need to get past the unusual aroma to reap the rewards of this beneficial blend.

INGREDIENTS

20grams Sweet Almond Oil

10grams Sesame Oil

10grams Nettle Extract

5grams Neem Oil

5grams Argan Oil

6 drops Orange Essential Oil

3 drops Lavender Essential Oil

3 drops Geranium Essential Oil

2 drops Sage Essential Oil

METHOD

1. Place oils and essential oils in TM and blend **90 seconds/50 degrees/speed 1**. While mixing slowly, add nettle extract.
2. Transfer to airtight container.

Application: Comb through dry hair, beginning at the roots and working down to the ends. If your hair is very dry and damaged apply liberally, otherwise apply lightly. Pull back or wrap in a towel and leave it on for anywhere from 30 minutes to 2 hours. Shampoo out with warm water. Repeat shampooing if necessary. Condition and style as usual.

CLAY HAIR MASK

MAKES: 1 application

TIME: 10 minutes

PACKAGING: Airtight container.

Use within 2 days.

Restore the health of your hair and scalp with this intensive mask. Bentonite clay moisturises and conditions, while the other ingredients work in synergy to cleanse, clarify, hydrate and heal.

INGREDIENTS

100grams Bentonite Clay

100grams Apple Cider Vinegar

35grams Sweet Almond Oil

20grams Coconut Oil

10 drops Argan Oil

METHOD

1. Melt coconut oil in TM **2 minutes/70 degrees/speed 2**.
2. Add other ingredients and mix **30 seconds/speed 2**.

Application: Comb through damp hair. Cover with cling wrap (or a towel.) Leave on for 20-30 minutes. Wash out with shampoo, rinse well. Condition and style as usual.

HAIR LIGHTENING SPRAY

MAKES: 265grams

TIME: 5 minutes

PACKAGING: Spray bottle. Use within 4 weeks.

Encourage your hair to go a shade or two lighter with this all-natural leave-in brightening spray.

INGREDIENTS

200grams Distilled Water

40grams Epsom Salt

10grams Vodka

10grams Aloe Vera Gel

5grams Lemon Juice

METHOD

1. Measure all ingredients into TM and mix **2 minutes/75 degrees/speed 2**. Check that all the salts have dissolved and if necessary mix again **1 minute/75 degrees/speed 2**.

2. Allow to cool. Use a funnel to fill bottle.

Application: Shake well before use. Lightly spray onto hair before going out into the sun. Condition and style as usual.

BEACH HAIR SPRAY

MAKES: 340grams

TIME: 5 minutes

PACKAGING: Spray bottle.

Use within 12 months.

Let your hair run wild with this economical and easy recipe. Your hair will have that just-back-from-the-beach look without you having to step foot on the sand.

INGREDIENTS

250grams Distilled Water

60grams Epsom Salt

10grams Sea Salt

10grams Aloe Vera Gel

5grams Jojoba Oil

5grams Solubilizer

METHOD

1. Measure water into TM and blend **3 minutes/80 degrees/ speed 1**.
2. Add all other ingredients and mix **1 minute/60 degrees/ speed 3**.
3. Allow to cool before bottling.

Application: Shake well before use. Mist onto to wet or dry hair, tousle through with hands and leave to dry naturally.

RESTORATIVE HAIR OIL

MAKES: 100grams

TIME: 5 minutes

PACKAGING: Dark glass bottle with eyedropper.

Use within 6 weeks.

All hair benefits from a pick-me-up now and then. This blend of oils is especially generous to hair and will add lustre and shine while repairing damage.

INGREDIENTS

50grams Coconut Oil

20grams Sesame Oil

20grams Sweet Almond Oil

10grams Neem Oil

1gram Essential Oil (I use 0.5grams each of Geranium and Cedarwood Atlas)

METHOD

1. Measure all ingredients into TM and combine **1 minute/50 degrees/speed 1**.
2. Use a funnel to transfer into bottle.

Application: Apply a few drops to dry hair and comb through. Leave on for 1-2 hours. Shampoo out, condition and style.

LICE COMBING SOLUTION

MAKES: 190grams

TIME: 5 minutes

PACKAGING: Airtight Container.

Use within 4 weeks

Head lice are the bane of every parent. Treating them effectively can be an ongoing drama that sometimes takes months to get under control. It doesn't have to be that way. This recipe will aid in the elimination of this pesky parasite. The combination of ingredients will paralyse crawlies and help nits and eggs slip easily from hair.

INGREDIENTS

160grams Light Olive Oil

25grams Dimethicone

3grams Eucalyptus Oil

2grams Clove Oil

2grams Peppermint Oil

1gram Rosemary Oil

METHOD

1. Combine all ingredients into TM and mix on **speed 3/30 seconds.**
2. Transfer into airtight container.

Application: Comb into hair until well covered. Use a nit comb to remove eggs, nits and lice. Shampoo hair. Repeat weekly until no eggs or lice are detected.

NO FRIZZ HAIR SPRITZ

MAKES: 210grams

TIME: 5 minutes

PACKAGING: Spray bottle. Use within 3 months.

Bad hair days will be a thing of the past with this super easy and supportive hair preparation. The jojoba oil will calm and replenish dry, stressed hair and encourage it to behave in a manageable fashion.

INGREDIENTS

100grams Distilled Water

50grams Aloe Vera Gel

25gram Jojoba Oil

25grams Glycerin

10grams Solubilizer

1gram Lavender Essential Oil

METHOD

1. Measure oil, glycerin, aloe vera gel, solubilizer and essential oil in TM and blend **20 seconds/speed 5**. Scrape down sides and blend **10 seconds/speed 2**.
2. Add water and mix **20 seconds/speed 3**.
3. Use a funnel to transfer into bottle.

Application: Shake well before each application. Mist onto frizzy or flyaway hair when required or after blow-drying. Leave in and style as usual.

HAIR REPAIR SPRITZ

MAKES: 330grams

TIME: 10 minutes

PACKAGING: Spray bottle. Use within 6 weeks.

Treat dull and lifeless locks with this restorative concoction of hair loving ingredients. The nettle extract and flax seeds work together to strengthen brittle fibres while the argan oil hydrates, protects and eliminates frizz and fly away.

INGREDIENTS

100grams Chamomile Floral Water (or Distilled Water)

150grams Distilled Water

20grams Nettle Extract

20grams Aloe Vera Gel

15grams Glycerin

10grams Flaxseeds

5grams Argan Oil

5grams Solubilizer

1gram Ginger Essential Oil

1.5grams Lavender Essential Oil

0.5grams Sage Essential Oil

NOTE: For a longer life, add 1% preservative.

METHOD

1. Measure water and flaxseeds into TM and cook **5 minutes/100 degrees/speed 0.5 reverse**. Discard seeds and set water aside.
2. Measure floral water, extract, aloe vera gel, solubilizer and glycerin into TM. Add flaxseed water and mix **30 seconds/50 degrees/speed 3**.
3. Add argan oil and essential oils and mix **10 seconds/ speed 4**.
4. Use a funnel to pour into containers.

Application: Shake well before each application. Mist lightly over wet or dry hair, style hair as usual.

SO SWEET HAIRSPRAY

MAKES: 300grams

TIME: 5 minutes

PACKAGING: Spray Bottle

Use within 6 weeks.

This recipe has been around for decades and was commonly made at home before the invention of commercial hair spays. The sugar will keep your hair in place without the nasty chemicals found in so many store-bought sprays.

INGREDIENTS

250grams Distilled Water

50grams White Sugar (increase to 100grams for a stronger hold)

METHOD

1. Measure sugar into TM and blend **15 seconds/speed 8**. Scrape down sides.
2. Add water and blend **4 minutes/80 degrees/speed 3**.
3. Allow to cool, and then use a funnel to pour into bottle.

Application: Style hair as desired and then mist over hair. Hair will feel a little sticky but the stickiness reduces as the spray dries.

Bath

Pamper yourself at bathtime with these simple to make and indulgent bath treats.

BLISSFUL BATH OIL

MAKES: 100grams

TIME: 5 minutes

PACKAGING: Glass bottle with cork stopper.

Use within 6-9 months.

Transform your next bath into a private blissful ritual with the addition of a teaspoon or two of this luxurious bath oil. The apricot kernel oil will leave your skin feeling soft and hydrated while the essential oils will restore your disposition and leave you feeling heavenly.

INGREDIENTS

100grams Apricot Kernel Oil

3grams Essential Oils of your choice*

*I like to use relaxing blends such as Lavender and Geranium (1.5grams of each.)

METHOD

1. Place all ingredients into TM. Blend **10 seconds/speed 4**.
2. Use a funnel to pour into containers.

Application: Add a teaspoon or two to running bath water. Lie back and relax. Caution: Take care when getting out of the bath after using this oil, as skin will be slippery.

DECADENT BATH MELTS

MAKES: approximately 12 pieces (15 grams each) though this will depend on the size of the mould used.

TIME: 20 minutes

PACKAGING: Store in airtight container. For gifting, package in cellophane bags or decorative glass jars.

ADDITIONAL TOOLS: Decorative silicon mould.

Use within 6 weeks.

Application: Drop one or two into warm running bath water. Hop in, lie back and enjoy!

Soothe your senses with these fragrant bathtime delights. Relax as they softly fizz and dissolve while infusing the water with conditioning ingredients. Variations for this recipe are endless. Try adding dried flower petals or finely ground oatmeal. For some fun colour them with mica. They also make fabulous and affordable handmade gifts.

INGREDIENTS

55grams Cocoa Butter

50grams Sodium Bicarbonate (Bi-carb Soda)

25grams Citric Acid

25grams Shea Butter

25grams Cornstarch

3grams Essential Oil*

*My favourite blend for this recipe is 1g Jasmine, 1g Sweet Orange and 1g Pettigrain.

METHOD

1. Measure butters in TM and melt **2 minute/60 degrees/ speed 1** (or until melted).
2. In a separate bowl combine dry ingredients and then place into TM with melted butters. Mix **20 seconds/speed 3**.
3. Add essential oil, petals and colouring (if using) mix **20 seconds/speed 2 reverse.**
4. Spoon into moulds, be sure that the mixture sinks completely in the cavity and press down lightly with back of spoon. Place into the fridge until hard.
5. When hard pop out of mould and package.

HEAVENLY BATH FIZZ

MAKES: 750grams

TIME: 5 minutes

PACKAGING: An airtight container.

Use within 6 months.

Let your worries bubble away with this decidedly delightful bath fizz. It is super easy to make and will leave your skin feeling soft and scented.

INGREDIENTS

300grams Sodium Bicarbonate (Bi-carb Soda)

175grams Citric Acid

125grams Fine Sea Salt

50grams Dried Herbs or Flowers (of your choice)

5grams Essential Oils of your choice*

*I like a blend of Ylang Ylang, Geranium and Rosewood.

METHOD

1. Measure salt, citric acid and bicarb into TM and blend **30 seconds/speed 4**.

2. Add essential oils and mix **20 seconds/speed 7**.

3. Add petals or herbs and mix **20 seconds/speed 0.5 reverse**.

Application: Add 2-3 tablespoons to warm bath, relax and let your troubles fizz away.

REVITALIZING BATH SALTS

MAKES: 250grams

TIME: 5 minutes

PACKAGING: Decorative airtight jar.

Use within 6 months.

Invigorate your body with these naturally revitalising minerals. The epsom salts ease aching muscles while the bi-carb soda softens the skin. Add your choice of essential oils to enliven or subdue the senses.

INGREDIENTS

100grams Coarse Sea Salt

100grams Epsom Salt (Magnesium Sulfate)

50grams Bi-carb Soda (Sodium Bicarbonate)

5grams Essential Oils of your choice

METHOD

1. Measure all ingredients into TM and blend **20 seconds/ speed 4.**
2. Place into container and seal.

Application: Place 1-2 tablespoons into warm running water, lie back and relax.

MUSCLE SOAK

MAKES: 300grams

TIME: 5 minutes

PACKAGING: Wide mouth, airtight jar.

Use within 12 months.

Let the aches and pains of a hard day's work ease away with this therapeutic selection of salts and essential oil.

INGREDIENTS

200grams Epsom Salt (Magnesium Sulfate)

50grams Sea Salt

50grams Bi-carb Soda (Sodium Bicarbonate)

2grams Peppermint Essential Oil

1gram Marjoram Essential Oil

0.5grams Clove Essential Oil

METHOD

1. Measure all ingredients into TM and mix **30 seconds/ speed 3.**

2. Spoon into containers. Store in a dry place.

Application: Scoop a generous spoonful into warm running bath water. Lie back and soak.

Creating Your Own Formulas

When you feel confident making these recipes, you may want to experiment with substituting ingredients and knocking up your own formulations. It is good practice to document the process so you can easily recreate it another time. The table on the opposite page can be photocopied and outlines the information you will need to record.

MEASURES & CONVERSIONS

DRY MEASURES

METRIC	IMPERIAL
15grams	1/2ounce
30grams	1ounce
60grams	2ounce
90grams	3ounce
125grams	4ounce (1/4lb)
155grams	5ounce
185grams	6ounce
220grams	7ounce
250grams	8ounce (1/2lb)
280grams	9ounce
315grams	10ounce
375grams	12ounce (3/4lb)
410grams	13ounce
440grams	14ounce
470grams	15ounce
500grams	16ounce (1lb)
750grams	24ounce (1.5lb)
1kilo	32ounce (2lb)

LIQIUD MEASURES

METRIC	IMPERIAL
30ml	1 fluid ounce
60ml	2 fluid ounce
90ml	3 fluid ounce
120ml	4 fluid ounce
150ml	5 fluid ounce
190ml	6 fluid ounce
250ml	8 fluid ounce
300ml	10 fluid ounce
500ml	16 fluid ounce
600ml	20 fluid ounce
1000ml	1.75 pints

SPOONS

	METRIC	IMPERIAL
1Tbs	20ml	0.67 fluid ounce
1tsp	5ml	0.16 fluid ounce
1/2tsp	2.5ml	0.08 fluid ounce
1/4tsp	1.25ml	0.04 fluid ounce

SUBSTITUTING INGREDIENTS Almost all oils can be substituted for another oil, as can some butters and clays. Though, keep in mind the individual oil properties and how this may affect the final product. Also, to avoid a failed batch remember to keep quantities the same.

Recipe:	
Date:	Total Quantity:
Amount:	Ingredients:
Steps:	
1.	
2.	
3.	
4.	
5.	
6.	

INVITATION

to join the Beauty Mix community

My wish is to encourage and inspire a community of skincare creators brought together by a passion to make wholesome, safe, nourishing skincare quickly, easily and affordably at home.

My aim is to share knowledge, guidelines and resources in order to motivate and empower you on this journey.

If this is an endeavour you think you would enjoy, then I invite you to join the ever-growing community of beauty mixers.

facebook.com/thebeautymix

pinterest.com/beautymixbook

twitter.com/GordonNickyg

The Beauty Mix Channel

thebeautymix.com.au

Wishing you loads of lovely beauty mixes, Nicky

CPSIA information can be obtained
at www.ICGtesting.com
Printed in the USA
BVHW02n0924160518
516150BV00010B/13/P
* 9 7 8 0 9 9 4 4 0 9 0 4 1 *